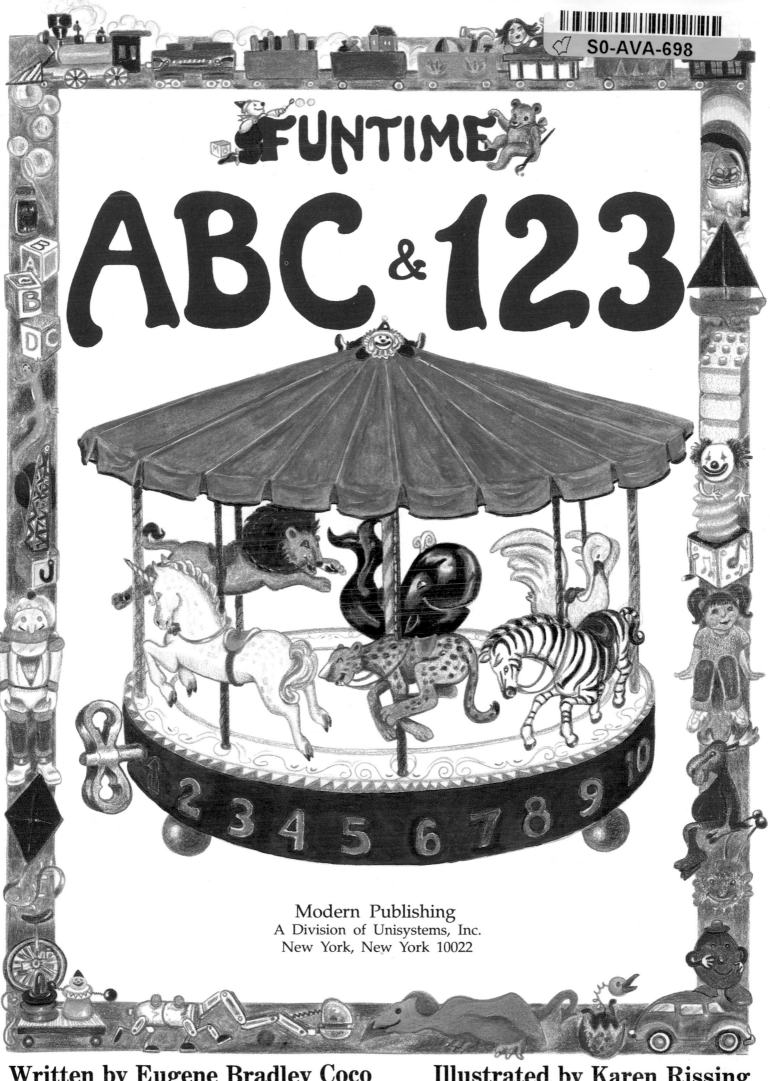

FUNTIME
ABC & 123

Modern Publishing
A Division of Unisystems, Inc.
New York, New York 10022

Written by Eugene Bradley Coco **Illustrated by Karen Rissing**

A toy store is the place to be
To learn your letters—A through Z!

Aa

AIRPLANES flying in the sky,

Bb

A BALL that bounces way up high,

Cc

CARS that zip across the floor,

Dd

DOLLS that talk and walk—and more!

Ee

An EASEL with a
brush or two;

Ff

FIRE ENGINES
zoom past you.

Gg

A baseball GLOVE
to catch and throw,

Hh

A HORSE to rock on
to and fro.

Ii

An INKWELL with a
pen, to write;

ink

Jj

JACK-IN-THE-BOX—
now that's a sight!

Kk

A KITE that glides up
to the sky,

Ll

A LASSO you can
throw or tie.

Mm

MARBLES flip into a can;

Nn

A pearly NECKLACE—very grand!

An OCTOPUS with legs galore;

PICK-UP-STICKS off of the floor.

Qq Be a QUEEN with a robe and crown

Rr Or jump a ROPE way up and down.

Ss

SOLDIERS lined up front to back;

Tt

See the TRAIN race down the track.

Uu

A toy UMBRELLA
for a rainy day;

Vv

The VIOLIN
is fun to play!

Ww

A WAGON filled with many toys,

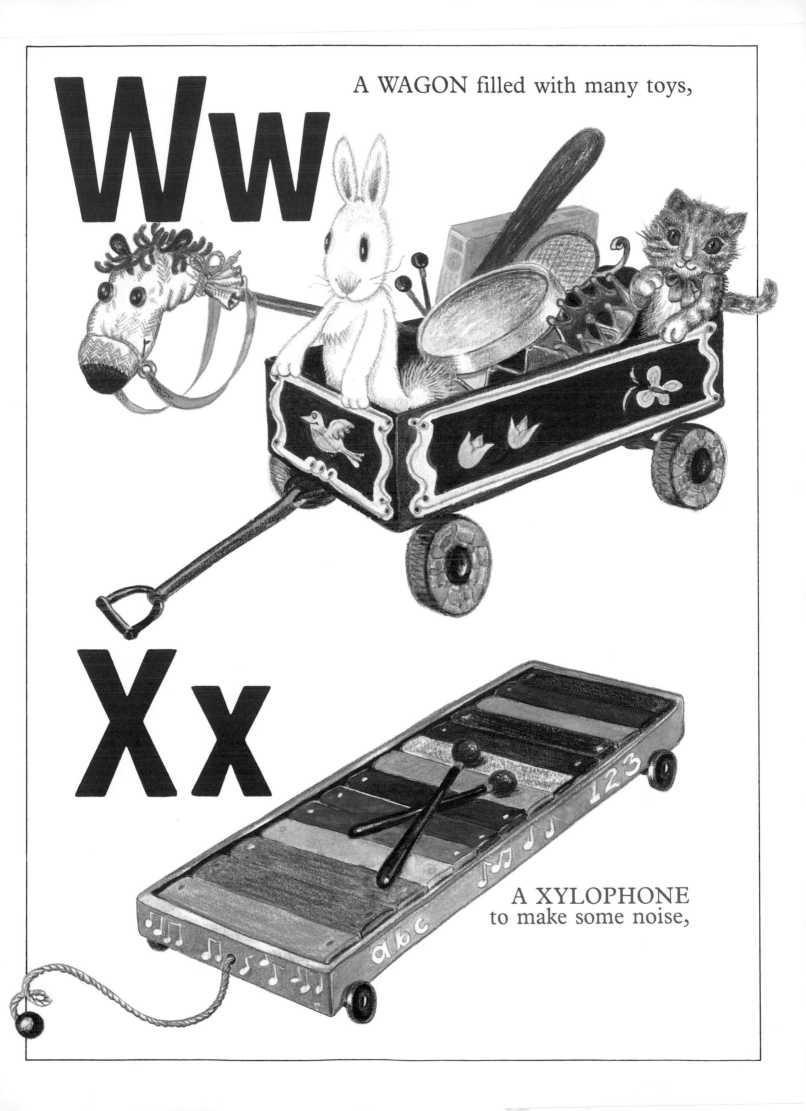

Xx

A XYLOPHONE
to make some noise,

Now pick your favorite toy and then
Turn the page and count to ten!

TOY STORE

1 2 3 4 5 6 7 8 9 10

1 Doll

2 Trains

3

Planes

4

Balls

5 Cars

6 Gloves

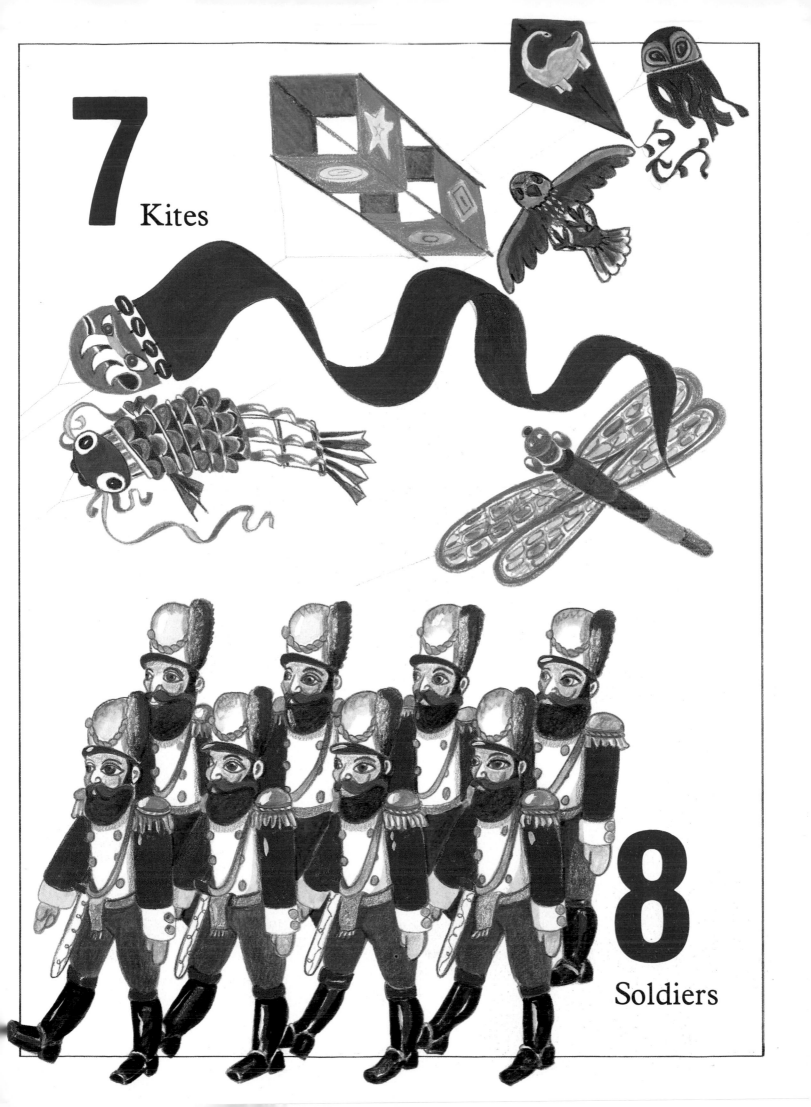

7
Kites

8
Soldiers

Violins

9

10

Toy Bears

So many things to learn
And so many things to see—
Don't you think a toy store is
A terrific place to be?